THE H

Hägar on the Rampage

by Dik Browne

ATTICA
PUBLICATIONS

Introducing . . .

HÄGAR THE HORRIBLE a hard-working Barbarian businessman. He's in sacking and looting.

His wife, HELGA. She finds civilising Hagar a 24-hour-a-day job!

This is HAMLET, their son, a real problem child! He insists on wearing his hair short, bathing, reading and otherwise behaving in a very unbarbarian manner.

HONI, their daughter, is sixteen years old, and still not married!

But that's not the end of Hagars troubles . . . there's also LUCKY EDDIE who must be the most hopeless assistant in history!

Attica Publications, an imprint of Argus Communications Ltd., DLM House, Edinburgh Way, Harlow, Essex CM20 2HL, England.

ISBN 1 85176 070 9

Printed and bound in Great Britain by Cox & Wyman Ltd, Reading

DIK BROWNE

DIK BROWNE

Look out for these forthcoming new exciting Hagar products in your loca giftshops and bookshops.

- ● Albums ● More Cartoon Books ●
- ● Wall Calendars ●
- ● Reminder Calendars ● Diaries ●
- ● Greeting Cards for all Occasions ●
- ● Postcards ● Posters ● Stick-Em-Ups ●
- ● Gift Wrap ● Gift Tags ●

For more details contact:
**Argus Communications Ltd.,
DLM House, Edinburgh Way, Harlow, Essex, CM20 2HL.
Tel: (0279) 39441.**